CARTOON NETWORK

ANNUAL 2005

Panini BOOKS

Cartoon Network Annual 2005 is published under license by Panini Publishing, a division of Panini UK Limited. Office of publication: Panini House, Coach and Horses Passage, The Pantiles, Tunbridge Wells, Kent TN2 5UJ. This publication may not be sold, except by authorised dealers, and is sold subject to the condition that it shall not be sold or distributed with any part of its cover or markings removed, nor in a mutilated condition. Printed in Italy. ISBN: 1-904419-30-5

WELCOME

NO NEED TO
RIP STRAIGHT INTO YOUR
2005 CARTOON NETWORK ANNUAL.
JUST SIT BACK, RELAX AND TAKE YOUR
TIME WHILST WE ADMINISTER AN AMPLE
DOSE OF TOON CRAZINESS...

contents

TV DINNER

HOLY SMOKE! THERE'S A PLETHORA OF TOON CRAZINESS GOING ON HERE. CAN YOU FIND ALL OF THESE GUYS, GIRLS AND OTHER CHARACTERS TOO UNSAVOURY TO MENTION, IN THE GRID BELOW? IT'S JUST THAT, WELL, WE CAN'T FIND 'EM...

- COW
- CHICKEN
- DEXTER
- DEE DEE
- RED GUY
- GRIM
- JOHNNY BRAVO
- MOJO JOJO
- BLOSSOM
- BUBBLES
- BUTTERCUP
- COURAGE

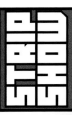

DEXTER'S LABORATORY

THIS IS THE LAST TIME I'M TELLING YOU IT'S *BEDTIME*, DEXTER.

AW, MOM! OKAY. I CAN FINISH MY WORK AT SCHOOL IN THE MORNING.

NO RUNNING OFF TO SCHOOL WITHOUT FINISHING YOUR CHORES IN THE MORNING!

MY *CHORES?* BUT I WANTED TO GET TO SCHOOL EARLY!

HMM... OKAY, MOM. I KNOW WHAT I MUST DO. GOODNIGHT!

SHORTLY AFTERWARD IN DEXTER'S LAB...

I THINK TWO DROPS SHOULD BE ENOUGH. MUST BE CAREFUL NOT TO OVERLOAD MY SYSTEM.

DRIP DRIP

EVEN LATER IN THE KITCHEN...

WITH THE ADDED SPEED FROM MY NEW *FAST-I-O'S* CEREAL I WILL BE ABLE TO GET MY CHORES DONE IN A FLASH AND STILL BE ABLE TO GET TO SCHOOL EARLY!

-*URP!*- IT MIGHT BE BETTER IF THEY WEREN'T QUITE SO *HEALTHY.*

-:HUFF! HUFF!:- HMM... IT DOESN'T SEEM TO HAVE WORKED.

I MUST HAVE MISCALCULATED SOMEWHERE. I'LL HAVE TO TRY AGAIN TOMORROW.

MORNING...

SO WHAT WILL IT BE, *DEE-DEE*? EGGS? FLAPJACKS?

WOOOO...! I WANT DEXTER'S NEW CEREAL.

SAY WHEN.

UMM... UMM... UMM--

WHEN!!

-:MUH!:- -:BLECH!:- NEED... SHUGAH!

NUMMY NUMS!

ROBBIE BUSCH- Writer
JOHN DELANEY- Penciller
JEFF ALBRECHT- Inker
JARED K FLETCHER- Letterer
SNO CONE- Colorist
HARVEY RICHARDS- Asst Editor
JOAN HILTY- Editor
DEXTER'S LABORATORY created
by GENNDY TARTAKOVSKY

WE MUST GO *FASTER!* DO *MORE!*

IT'S A GOOD THING I WAS PREPARED. ONWARD, DEE-DEE! LET'S TAKE A LEETLE TRIP!

HOO-HOO-HOO!!! HOO-HOO!

I MUST FIND SOME REALLY SUPER SPECTACULAR THINGS FOR DEE-DEE TO DO TO BURN OFF SOME OF THE EXCESS ENERGY.

AFRICA...

MY INFORMATION-GATHERING INSTRUMENTS HAVE PICKED UP A DISTURBANCE HERE.

OKAY, DEE-DEE, YOU SEE THE PRETTY ELEPHANTS? YOU HAVE TO RUN AROUND THEM IN A CIRCLE UNTIL THEY STOP STAMPEDING!

UH-UH-UH-OKAY! CAN I GO NOW, PLEASE?!

ROAR

APROOOROOO

ROAR

ROAR

CONTINUED ON PAGE 16

HOW TO DRAW... DEXTER

WARNING:
ALWAYS ASK AN ADULT TO HELP YOU IF YOU'RE USING SCISSORS. WHAT? YOU DON'T NEED SCISSORS TO DRAW? OK, FORGET THAT LAST BIT.

STEP 1

You might think that drawing is all about being artistic, but you would be wrong. You must be scientific! Observe that this is the proportion of my compact but powerful body and my huge brain.

STEP 2

Using your calculations from step 1, you can now see that the outline of the world's greatest scientist is appearing. My strong jawline and nimble feet can now be accurately positioned.

STEP 3

Now that the shapes that make up my biological construction are functional. You can see where my ears, hands and glasses should be placed for optimum scientific usage.

STEP 4

It is important to be veeeery accurate with the fine details. I myself am always extremely careful, which is why my experiments almost never go horribly wrong. You should learn from this.

STEP 5

When you are satisfied that your work is completely accurate, you can erase your working lines. Your portrait of myself is almost complete and you will have triumphed in your task!

STEP 6

Finally you can colour in your masterpiece and place it somewhere in your home where people will be able to see clearly that I, Dexter, am not only a genius but also a handsome and noble creature!

15

CONTINUED FROM PAGE 12

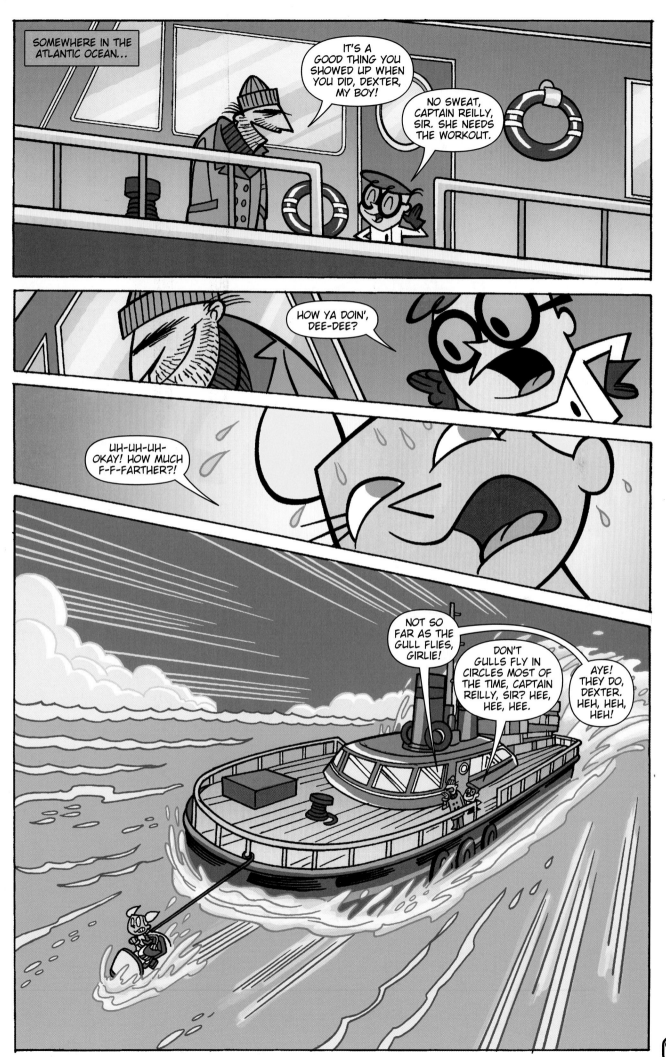

DEXTER'S LAB.

NAPTIME, DEE-DEE. WHEN THE TIMER GOES OFF YOU WILL HAVE FORGOTTEN ALL ABOUT OUR ADVENTURES. YOU WILL BE BACK TO NORMAL-- OR AT LEAST NORMAL FOR *YOU.*

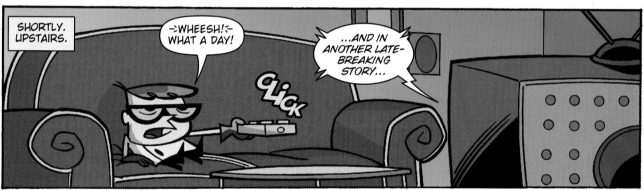

SHORTLY. UPSTAIRS.

~WHEESH!~ WHAT A DAY!

CLICK

...AND IN ANOTHER LATE-BREAKING STORY...

...A SMALL VILLAGE IN THE AFRICAN BUSH WAS SAVED FROM AN ELEPHANT STAMPEDE BY WHAT THE NATIVES ARE CALLING *HURRICANE DEE-DEE...*

...AND A THE S.S. BULLDOG WAS *PULLED* INTO THE HARBOR BY A PEDAL BOAT?

HEY, DEXTER! YER DROOLING!

WANNA PLAY, DEXTER?

I'LL RACE YA TO THE SWING SET.

RACE?! ARE YOU CRAZY?!

WHAT'S HAPPENING IN HERE, KIDS?

DEXTER SAYS I'M CRAZY BECAUSE I WANT TO PLAY ON THE SWINGS WITH HIM.

THAT'S *NOT* WHAT I WAS SAYING.

WELL, DEXTER CAN'T PLAY RIGHT NOW... HE HAS TO *FINISH* HIS *CHORES.*

THE END

I.R. EATING

I.R. saying you guess what I.R. been eating

I.M. Weasel has a superior intellect, capable of mastering the most complex skills and mental challenges. Unfortunately, I.R. Baboon is the exact opposite. If this were Weasels' page, no doubt he would be asking you questions on agebraic formulation. But it seems instead, we must play one of I.R.'s favourite games, entitled "Guess what I've eaten". Oh dear. Skip the page if you are beyond this challenge...

1 Liking much the catching of these.

2 It R meaty smell, but not being from the sea.

3 I.R.'s brothers eating lot of these.

5 MMmm I.R. could eat whole string of them.

4 I.R. not sure that edible, but ate anyway.

a

b

c

d

e

I AM WEASEL

ANSWERS: 1-C 2-A 3-D 4-E 5-B

I AM WEASEL.™

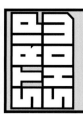

I.R. BEING SICK OF BEING COLD AND STARVING!

SHHHHHH. WHEN ONE CAN ONLY AFFORD *SNOWBALLS* AS BAIT, ONE MUST BE *VERY* PATIENT.

I.R. THINKING *BETTER WAY* BE USING SPECIAL FISH CALLS! *HERE FISHY, FISHY, HERE*--

NO, NO, YOU *FOOL!* LOUD NOISE SCARES THEM AWAY. BESIDES--

CRACK

PLIP   PLOP

OH NO-- WE'RE STUCK!

LEAST I.R. ABLE TO BE *SCREAMING...*

HELP!!!

PLEASE, BABOON-- YOUR PLAINTIVE WAIL IS MAKING IT DIFFICULT FOR ME TO CONCENTRATE. I SIMPLY *MUST* FIND A WAY TO CONSTRUCT A DISTRESS FLARE FROM OUR COOKING KIT...

...BEFORE GOING INTO SHOCK FROM COLD... LOSING CONSCIOUSNESS...

...OOOH!

SEVERAL DAYS LATER...

AAAAAHHH!!!

OHHHH, *WONDERFUL,* YOU'RE *AWAKE.* LOVE TO STAY AND *CHAT,* BUT I HAVE A *PRESS CONFERENCE* TO ATTEND.

WHAT--?! *A HOSPITAL!* WE *WERE* SAVED! IT'S A GOOD THING THAT I'M A SLEEPWALKER. I MUST HAVE CONTINUED TO CONSTRUCT THE FLARE WHILE I WAS UNCONSCIOUS. THIS IS *WONDERFUL,* THIS IS *INCREDIBLE,* THIS IS... *UNCOMFORTABLE.*

WHAT'S THAT *EXTRA FULL* FEELING BEHIND ME?!

UHHHHHHH.

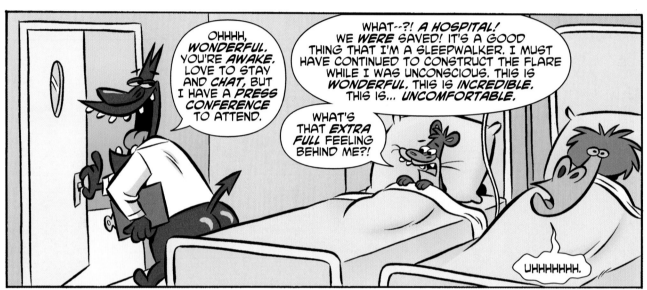

WEASEL IS THE BEST AT WHATEVER HE PUTS HIS MIND TO, AND THE WORLD LOVES HIM FOR THAT... THAT IS EVERYONE EXCEPT I.R. BABOON. HE'LL DO ANYTHING-- AND WE MEAN ANYTHING-- TO STEAL THE GLORY FROM...

I.M. WEASEL
in
WALK A MILE IN MY GLUTES

SCOTT CUNNINGHAM- Writer
MIKE KAZALEH- Artist

JARED FLETCHER- Letterer
HEROIC AGE- Colorist
HARVEY RICHARDS- Asst. Editor
JOAN HILTY- Editor

I AM WEASEL created by
DAVID FEISS

I.R. WONDERING WHY SLEEPING ON BACK NOW BEING SO EASY!

NOOOOO!

I'VE GOT *BABOON'S BUTT!*

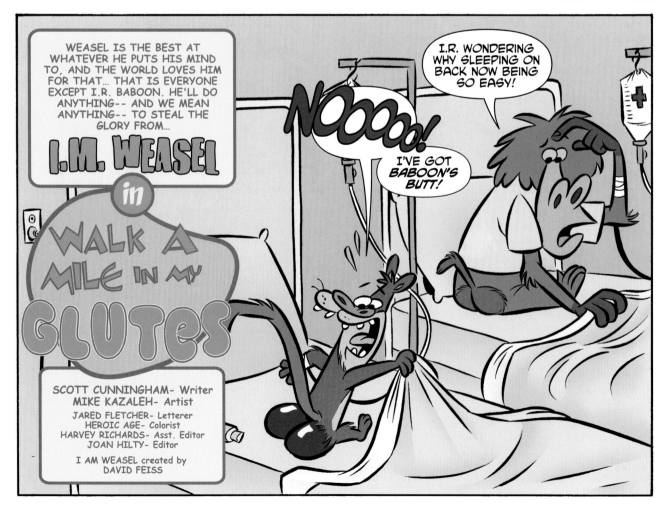

SEVERAL MONTHS LATER...

MR. HOST, BABOON SIR, BEFORE AMERICA'S MOST POPULAR NEW GAME SHOW BEGINS TONIGHT, I WOULD LIKE TO OBSERVE THAT YOUR BACKSIDE IS *SIMPLY INCOMPARABLE.*

AND ADORING FANS BEING SURE TO KNOW I.R. *ALWAYS* THIS WAY BEEN LOOKING!

CELEBRITY BACKSIDE

ALWAYS!

I SUPPOSE THE ULTIMATE IRONY IS THAT, AFTER THE OPERATION, WE *BOTH* WOUND UP IN SHOW BUSINESS.

I CHOOSE CELEBRITY ANIMAL COUPLES FOR $200!

Powder

WHILE THAT LUCKY APE HAS BECOME A *POPULAR TV PERSONALITY...*

I'VE SUNK TO A LOWLY...

LOOK AT HIS *BUTT.*

IT'S *FUNNY!*

WHAM!

...RODEO CLOWN!

SEVERAL SECONDS LATER (BUT SEVERAL MILES AWAY)...

≶SIGH≷ I ALWAYS FEEL *SOOOO EMPTY* AFTER *CELEBRITY BACKSIDES MATCH GAME* ENDS. PERHAPS THIS NATURE SPECIAL WILL HELP HOLD BACK THAT CRUSHING LONELINESS FOR *ONE MORE HOUR.*

SNIFF

HMMM...THAT CREATURE LOOKS FAMILIAR.

OF COURSE, THE WEASEL IS *BEST KNOWN* FOR ITS LONG, SLENDER BODY.

OH, THIS IS *TERRIBLE.* WHEN PEOPLE SEE THIS, MY REPUTATION WILL BE *TOAST!*

PLASMATRON

BUT THEN THIS *IS* PUBLIC TELEVISION. THERE'S A *GOOD CHANCE* I'M THE *ONLY ONE* WATCHING. BUT THEN WHAT IF THEY START ONE OF THOSE ANNOYING FUND-RAISER MARATHONS. *I'M DOOMED!!!*

UNLESS...

SO LET ME GET THIS STRAIGHT-- YOU WANT TO OPERATE *AGAIN* AND GIVE ME MY BOTTOM BACK. ONLY *FIRST,* BECAUSE BABOON WOULD NEVER SWITCH BACK VOLUNTARILY, WE HAVE TO POSE AS AUTOGRAPH- SEEKING FANS AND *KIDNAP HIM???*

A LITTLE COMPLICATED-- BUT THAT'S *RIIIIGHT.* ALTHOUGH I *REEEEALLY* WOULD JUST *LOVE* HIS AUTOGRAPH!

BACKSTAGE

≶SIGH≷ SO MANY FANS FOR MEETING I.R. HANGING AROUND AGAIN.

FAME IS SOMETIMES BIG PAIN IN THE...

PLEASE, PLEASE, PLEASE, PICK MEEEEEE FIRST!

KLONK!

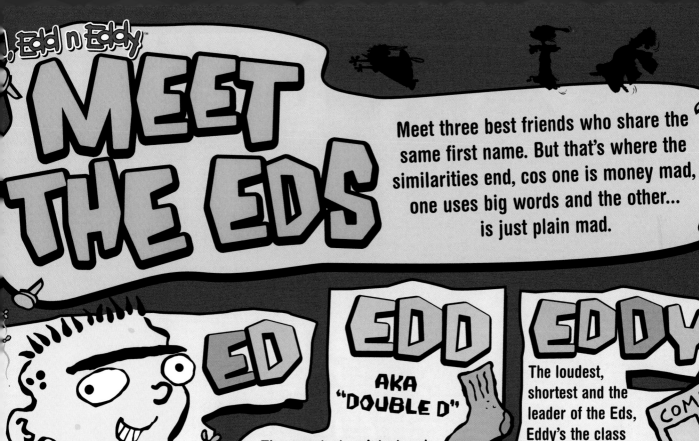

Ed, Edd n Eddy
MEET THE EDS

Meet three best friends who share the same first name. But that's where the similarities end, cos one is money mad, one uses big words and the other... is just plain mad.

ED

The smelliest, tallest and best at attracting flies, Ed likes "B" monster movies and model kits. He's got an annoying sister (Sarah) and breaks out in rashes. Often.

EDD
AKA "DOUBLE D"

The smartest, quietest and neatest. He labels everything and doesn't want anyone touching his stuff. Often prone to major crushes on girls, he likes to send them socks as a token of his affection.

EDDY

The loudest, shortest and the leader of the Eds, Eddy's the class clown with the money-making schemes and fly-away hair. Currently possess the secret recipe for the "El Mongo Stink Bomb."

COMIC

5¢

25¢

10¢

5¢

5 THINGS YOU NEVER KNEW ABOUT THE EDS...

1 EDD WAS ONCE STALKED BY ED'S SISTER, SARAH.

2 ED'S THREE FAVOURITE FOODS ARE GRAVY, BUTTERED TOAST AND BIG CAKES.

3 ED IS ALLERGIC TO GUINEA PIGS.

4 EDD'S PARENTS HAVE NEVER BEEN SEEN. THEY LEAVE HIM POST-IT NOTES AROUND THE HOUSE.

5 EDDY HAS AN OLDER BROTHER WHO WAS "SENT AWAY."

29

MICHAEL KRAIGER—writer
VINCENT DEPORTER—penciller
ANGUS BUNGAY—inker
JENNA GARCIA—letterer
DIGITAL CHAMELEON—colorist
HARVEY RICHARDS—asst. editor
JOAN HILTY—editor
ED ED n EDDY created by DANNY ANTONUCCI

DCCC27

KND
CODENAME: KIDS NEXT DOOR™

COMMAND ROOM

Five extraordinary 10-year-olds, who are dedicated to freeing all children from the tyrannical rule of adults, have formed a covert team. They are... Codename Kids Next Door!

While testing a super growth power radiated seed, the KND accidentally grew a giant tree straight through the middle of Numbuh One's parent's house and decided to build their treehouse there. Numbuh One's parents didn't seem to notice.

TREEHOUSE HQ

CODENAME:	NUMBUH ONE	
AKA: Nigel Uno	Description: The leader	
Speciality: SUPREME COMMANDERNESS		

TOP SECRET SURVEILLANCE

CODENAME:	NUMBUH TWO	
AKA: Hoagie P. Gilligan Jr.	Description: The genius	
Speciality: AIR SUPERIORITY		

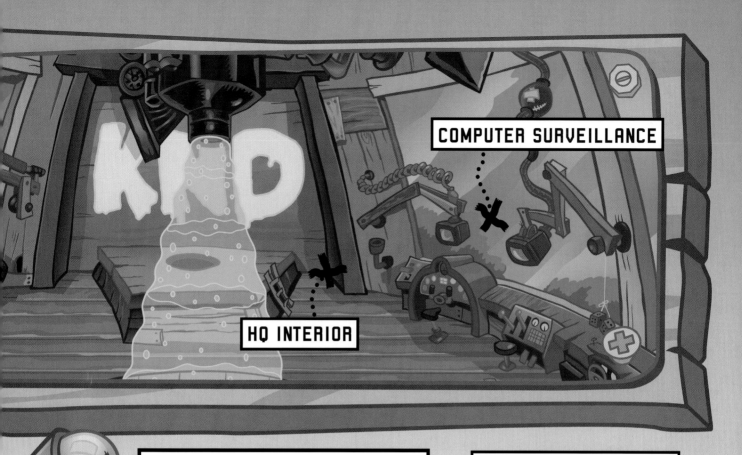

COMPUTER SURVEILLANCE

HQ INTERIOR

VILLAIN PROFILES...

LOCATION: Down the lane.

THE DELIGHTFUL CHILDREN FROM DOWN THE LANE.

Subjects known as arch rivals of the KND due to their deviousness and good manners. Subjects will do anything grown-ups tell them to do. Or worse.

CODENAME: *NUMBUH THREE*

AKA: *Kuki Sanban* | **Description:** *The flirt*

Speciality: DIVERSIONARY TACTICS

CODENAME: *NUMBUH FOUR*

AKA: *Wallabee Beatles* | **Description:** *The tough kid*

Speciality: HAND-TO-HAND COMBAT

CODENAME: *NUMBUH FIVE*

AKA: *Abigail Lincoln* | **Description:** *The quiet one*

Speciality: STEALTH-LIKE TACTICS

BRAIN

REMEMBER ME?

Ed, Edd n Eddy

Poor Ed has forgotten everyone's name. Again. Can you find them all in the grid of remembrance?

A	R	B	O	J	G	D	Y	D	D	E
J	O	H	N	N	Y	Q	E	P	R	H
F	L	P	K	Z	R	T	V	D	O	M
J	F	A	R	E	H	A	P	N	D	K
I	L	M	V	A	V	J	L	R	E	E
A	A	H	T	H	B	I	A	G	F	I
N	L	Q	W	L	O	M	N	L	I	R
D	O	E	D	O	N	M	K	T	J	A
B	M	A	E	M	A	Y	N	Z	G	M
P	J	K	Q	S	Z	L	O	R	N	N
G	I	S	A	R	A	H	E	P	D	H

JOHNNY SARAH

KEVIN PLANK LEE

MAY MARIE

JIMMY

ROLF NAZ

EDDY

EDD

MINDFUL

Dexter's mind-reading machine is, at last complete. Can you aid him in operating the machine and find out what Dee Dee is thinking of?

e P!

n

O S

Dexter's Laboratory

SQUEEZERS

POWER PASTING

Last time we looked, Mojo Jojo was taking a pasting from The Powerpuff Girls. Oh, he still is. Can you spot seven differences between these two shots of the ruckus?

ANSWERS: Mindful: PONIES; Power Pasting: Buttercup's swoosh; Blossom's hair-bow; Mojo's helmet patch; Mojo's Ear; Buttercup's hair; Bubbles' pigtail; Buttercup's arm. Commence Transmission: Knight Brace is on the loose.

COMMENCE TRANSMISSION...

CODENAME: KIDS NEXT DOOR

A top-secret transmission has been intercepted by Numbah Five. Can you decipher the code and rush it up to Numbah One?

○	↙	⟲	■	★	□

‡	V	⟲	*	↖

⟲	)(

:	↙

□	★	↖

↘	:	:	)(	↖

A	⟲	N	↙
B	‡	O	:
C	*	P	!
D	Λ	Q	●
E	↖	R	V
F	+	S	)(
G	■	T	□
H	★	U	\
I	⟲	V	«
J	=	W	⧺
K	○	X	/
L	↘	Y	॥
M	»	Z	↗

COW and CHICKEN

CAPTAIN CHICKEN

SCOTT CUNNINGHAM--WRITER
TIM HARKINS--ARTIST
JENNA GARCIA--LETTERER
DIGITAL CHAMELEON--COLORIST
HARVEY RICHARDS--ASST. EDITOR
JOAN HILTY--EDITOR
COW & CHICKEN CREATED BY DAVID FEISS

LOOK WHO'S BEIN' RESCUED-- *AGAIN!*

¡USE MÁS PRECAUCIÓN, LA PRÓXIMA VEZ, PARA QUE NO SUELTE LAS FUERZAS DEL DEMONIO!*

*YOU MUST HAVE CAUTION, NEXT TIME, AND NOT UNLEASH MUCH EVIL FORCES!

WHAT-EVER...

I *HEARD* DAT CRACK, PAL! JEST WAT IS YA SAYIN'? DAT DIS IS GITTIN' *BOARD*-ING?

YOUSE *IS* DA ONE *ALWAYS* SAVED, AIN'T YA?

EVER TRY TA DO SOMETHIN' FER *YA-SELF*, YA *BIG GIRL!*

THEY IS JUST *WIBBING* YOU, SWEET BWUDDAH. DON'T LISTEN TO THEMS!

SPEAKIN' O' *BIG GIRLS*-- LOOK WHO'S COMIN' TA DA RESCUE *NOW!*

YEH, NEXT TIME LET YER LITTLE *SISTER* SAVE YA!

GEEZ, TANKS FER MAKIN' IT *WORSE!*

OH BWUDDAH, IF YOU EVER NEED A SHOULDER OF *BEEF* TO CRY ON...

NO! LEAVE ME ALONE TO WALLOW IN MY OWN *DE-FUNK-TION!*

¿SIGH¿ I GOTTA LEARN TA TAKE CARE OF PROBLEMS *MYSELF.*

BUTS *HOW?*

IF ONLY DERE WUZ SOME *SIGN!*

THWACK

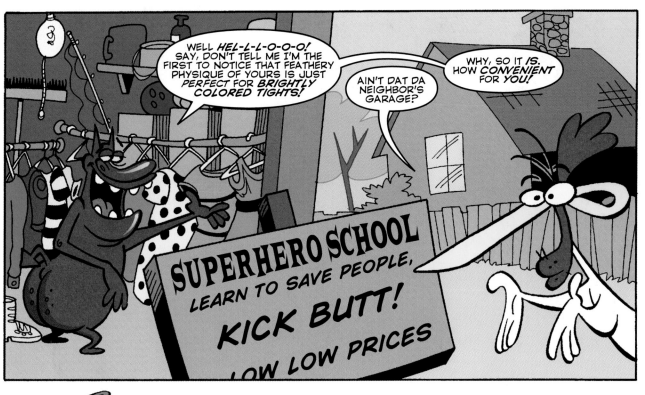

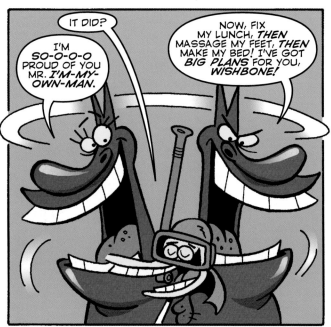

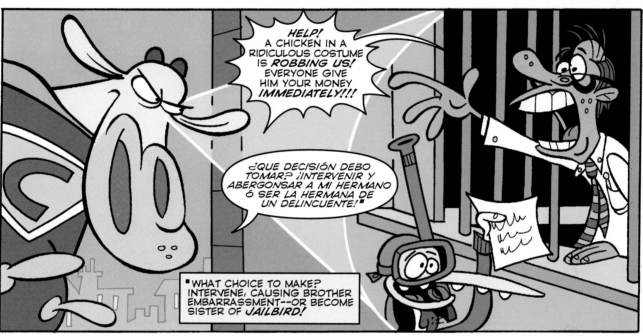

Dear Johnny,
When I go to the chemists to buy hair gel I get embarrassed and end up buying zit cream or athlete's foot powder. I'm sure the chemist knows I want hair gel to impress girls. How can I get over my awkwardness?

Carson Swindells
Hairtlepool

VAT o' HAIR GEL

Dear Carson
Hair gel is nothing to be ashamed about. It makes you look – studly! Sure, you may spend some time alone in the bathroom experimenting, but the mamaçitas will sure appreciate the ol' squeeze-squirt-slide stance once you've perfected it. And if you still have problems buying it yourself – get your momma to pick it up. Ah do.

Dear Johnny,
My girlfriend won't write, won't return calls and doesn't meet me when I arrange to go on a date with her. Have I done something wrong?

Lee Depp-Hearted
Milton Notsokeene

Dear Lee Depp-Hearted
Whooaa, spooky! Either you haven't talked to this chick and told her that you dig her, in which case you're a spooky stalker, so stop it. Or you're, like, dead and she can't see you. In which case why aren't you haunting the girls' changing rooms?

JOHNNY BRAVO™

Dear Johnny,
My boyfriend has appalling table manners. It's our four-week anniversary next week and I want him to take me out for a romantic candle-lit dinner. What can I do?

Ethel Furtburger
Ham-On-Rye

Dear Ethel,
Food is >scoff< important to us >chomp< guys. You can't >scarff< get between a man >gobble< and his >munch< food. Learn to >smack< live with it or >shlurp< say 'Pasta la vista, baby'.

THE POWERPUFF GIRLS

THE CITY OF TOWNSVILLE. HOME TO THREE GIRLS WITH EXTRAORDINARY POWERS... AND A MONKEY WITH A BIG BRAIN, POINTY TEETH AND SUSPECT TASTE IN FOOTWEAR. NOT FORGETTING THE KINDLY SOUL IN A WHITE LABCOAT WHO STARTED THE WHOLE SHABANGLE, WHO'LL REMAIN NAMELESS. UNTIL WE REVEAL THAT HE'S CALLED PROFESSOR UTONIUM.

PROFESSOR UTONIUM WAS A LONELY SCIENTIST WHOSE LIFELONG DREAM WAS TO CREATE THE PERFECT LITTLE GIRL.

KABLOOM!

MIXING THE INGREDIENTS SUGAR, SPICE AND EVERYTHING NICE TOGETHER, HIS CONCOCTION WAS NEARLY COMPLETE...

BUT THEN, HE ACCIDENTALLY ADDED A DASH OF THE TOXIC CHEMICAL X!

AND THUS THE POWERPUFF GIRLS WERE BORN!

IT'S UP TO THE POWERPUFF GIRLS TO PROTECT TOWNSVILLE FROM THE FORCES OF EVIL! GO GIRLS, GO!

blossom

WELCOME TO TOWNSVILLE

THIRD   PALM

WARNING
DO NOT APPROACH

TOWNSVILLE IS A LOVELY PLACE. THAT IS, IF YOU CAN TURN A BLIND EYE TO THE BUG-EYED MONSTERS, CRIMINAL SUPER-BADDIES AND QUESTIONABLY INEPT MAYOR. NICE PARK, THOUGH.

PPG HOUSE ▶

bubbles

DID YA KNOW?

* Blossom is the leader of The Powerpuff Girls

* Buttercup once had a crush on Ace, the leader of the Gangreen Gang.

* Fuzzy Lumpkins was once voted in as Mayor just by shouting a lot. It didn't last long.

* All of The Powerpuff Girls hate eating broccoli.

* Mojo Jojo was Professor Utonium's first creation.

buttercup

SAY IT AIN'T SO

HIDDEN IN THE GRID OF HIDING, THERE ARE SOME PHRASES THAT MOJO JOJO WILL PROBABLY NEVER SAY. SO YOU'D BETTER FIND THEM ALL, OR HE'LL START TALKING ALL WEIRD ON US...

A	D	O	R	A	B	L	E	A	D
D	R	S	C	W	X	O	F	O	A
N	E	K	O	Q	H	V	L	D	R
I	A	E	J	R	S	E	U	S	L
K	M	G	S	K	R	L	F	B	I
C	Y	S	O	F	T	Y	F	C	N
D	U	O	W	V	X	E	Y	H	G
H	S	T	S	N	A	P	P	Y	K
Z	Q	E	I	S	H	Q	J	O	K
B	S	P	R	E	T	T	Y	Y	K

LOVELY

KIND

SORRY

PRETTY

FLUFFY   ADORABLE   DARLING

SNAPPY   SOFTY   DREAMY

CUTIE

TELL IT TO THE MAYOR

The Mayor of Townsville can halt crime with one simple, sweeping movement. No, not with a broom, but by phoning The Powerpuff Girls. But who's to blame for the latest wave of petty, low-down, sneaky, underhand wrongdoing? Read the statements of the Townsville townspeople's eyewitness accounts and see if you can reveal the identities of these dastardly wrongdoers...

SUSPECT A

MOST WANTED!

SUSPECT C

SUSPECT D

SUSPECT B

SUSPECT

Grubber wos ere

1 She had the most totally awesome curly hair I ever saw! And I was like, soooo transfixed by it, that I didn't noticed she'd stolen my mother! And then she's was outta there like, someone who could disappear real quick.

3 This guy, he snatched my favourite earmuffs right off my head. And he was dribbling an' his eyes was a poppin' out and his skin was like, slimy an' green.

2 Man oh Man. I'm buying some stuff from the store when these three dudes wobble in and try to raid the cash register. I say "try" cos, man, they were the sloppiest criminals I ever saw. They left empty handed.

4 He had this awfully high-pitched voice that quite put me off my sushi. And then he had the audacity to change my sushi into an over-sized monster from the sea. Only we weren't in the sea. We were in Townsville.

5 He zapped me with this electro ray that made me speak in a high pitched voice, right before I had an interview. Boy was I mad! He was like, this little animal man, like an ape or chimp or something.

52

JOHNNY BRAVO

HURRY UP, JOHNNY! IT'S ABOUT TO COME ON!

C'MON, LITTLE SUZY. JOHNNY DOESN'T WANNA WATCH TEEVEE.

I WAS GOING OUT TO PICK UP BABES!

BUT THIS IS THE BEST TV SHOW EVER! AND YOU PROMISED!

AW, MAN! IT'S 2-FOR-1 DAY AT THE MALL, AND IF THAT MEANS WHAT I THINK IT DOES...

SHHHHH!

A LONG TIME AGO, IN THE AGE OF APOCRYPHA, THERE LIVED A WARRIOR. ONCE SHE WAS BAD. NOW SHE RIDES ON THE SIDE OF GOOD. BUT SHE HATES BAD SO MUCH SHE'S SWORN TO SMITE IT REPEATEDLY WITH THE COLD STEEL OF HER RAZOR-SHARP SWORD...

JOHNNY HATES CHICK SHOWS.

RED XONIA WARRIOR SHE-DEVIL!

DWAYNE McDUFFIE-WRITER ANTHONY WILLIAMS-PENCILLER JIM AMASH-INKER DAVE TANGUAY-COLORIST PHIL FELIX-LETTERER HARVEY RICHARDS-ASSISTANT EDITOR HEIDI MacDONALD & JOAN HILTY-EDITORS

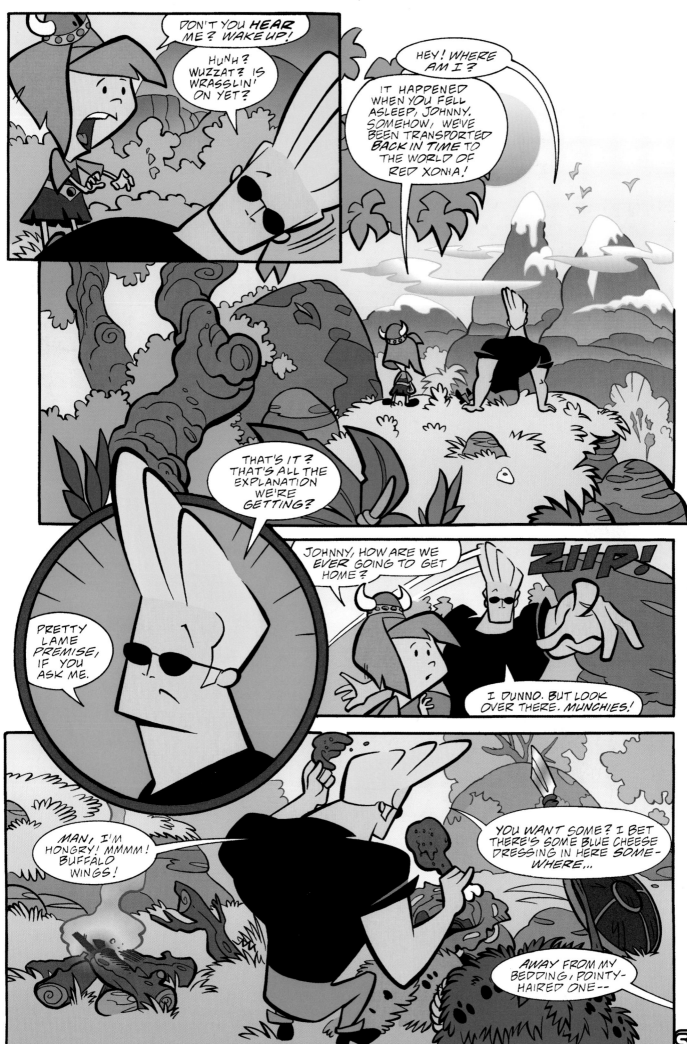

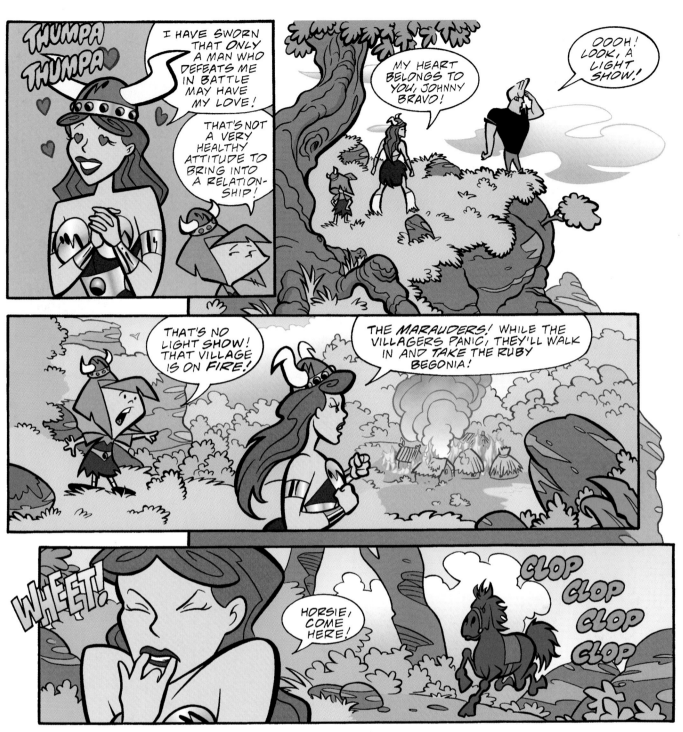

THUMPA THUMPA

I HAVE SWORN THAT *ONLY* A MAN WHO *DEFEATS* ME IN *BATTLE* MAY HAVE MY LOVE!

THAT'S NOT A VERY *HEALTHY* ATTITUDE TO BRING INTO A *RELATIONSHIP!*

MY HEART BELONGS TO *YOU,* JOHNNY BRAVO!

OOOH! LOOK, A *LIGHT SHOW!*

THAT'S NO *LIGHT SHOW!* THAT VILLAGE IS ON *FIRE!*

THE *MARAUDERS!* WHILE THE VILLAGERS PANIC, THEY'LL WALK IN AND *TAKE THE RUBY BEGONIA!*

WHEET!

HORSIE, COME HERE!

CLOP CLOP CLOP CLOP

IF YOU ARE *AFRAID,* YOU SHOULD STAY BEHIND. I WILL RETURN FOR YOU!

LISSEN UP, CANDY APPLES.

JOHNNY DOESN'T KNOW THE MEANING OF THE WORD *FEAR!*

THAT IS *GOOD,* MY LOVE. THE TWO OF US WILL BE *ALONE* AGAINST OVER *THREE DOZEN* BLOOD-CRAZED MARAUDERS!

OH, *"FEAR."* COME TO THINK OF IT, I *DO* KNOW THAT ONE!

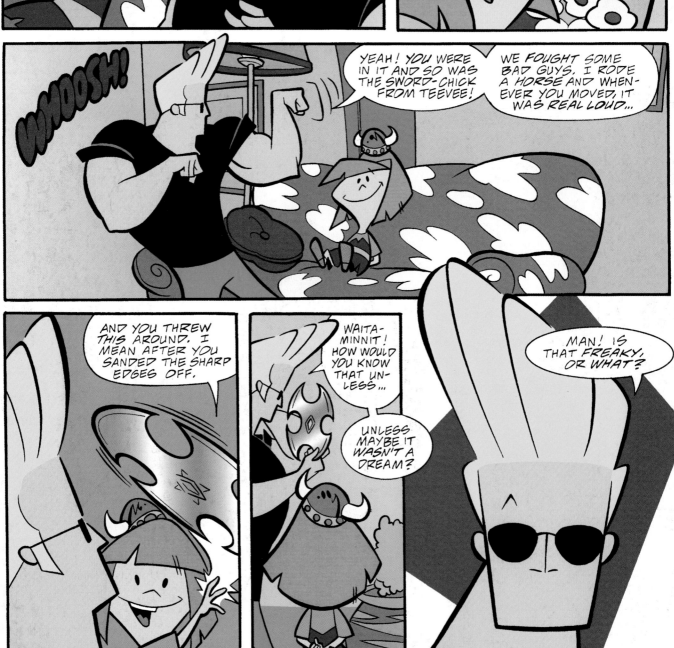